Michael Bentine's

Big Potty Fun Book

Written
and Illustrated
by
Michael Bentine

Futura Publications Limited
Robson Books

First published in paperback in Great Britain
in 1974 jointly by Futura Publications Ltd.
(49 Poland Street, London W1A 2LG) and Robson
Books Ltd. (28 Poland Street, London W1V 3DB),
and simultaneously in hardback by Robson Books.

ISBN 0 8600 7135 9

Editor: Elizabeth Rose
Designer: David Ross

Printed and bound in Great Britain by
Redwood Burn Limited, Trowbridge & Esher

Written and illustrated by
Michael Bentine

Robson Books/Futura Publications

WARNING

Hello and a very warm welcome to Michael Bentine's Big Potty Fun Book! But before you start reading it, here is a special warning — watch out or you may catch Pottymania! Let me explain.

The World Health Organization (or *WHO?* as it is known for short), has reported that people all over the world are going down with a mysterious ailment called Pottymania. Our own Potty medical specialist, Doctor Pottle, tells me that Pottymania (or going Potty) is indeed very contagious (that means catching — though I've never heard of anyone contaging a ball). It affects grown-ups just as much as it does boys and girls (or, to be more polite, girls and boys). However, Doctor Pottle assures me that there's nothing to worry about, and it's really quite harmless.

He says the first signs or symptoms of Pottymania are that you begin to stare very hard at your friends, and while you're looking at them, hey presto! — they suddenly turn into Pottys. Of course, they don't *really* turn into Pottys, because real Pottys are only fourteen inches high on average (that is, when a medium-sized Potty draws himself up to his full height). But they just *look* like them! Their noses grow bigger and bigger, and their hair grows down over their eyes, just like Pottys!

The next symptom is that you start talking in Potty voices, and muttering strange Potty expressions, such as 'Them little nurdling nigh nigglums,' or 'It makes me mad mad mad mad mad!'

Another sure sign you've got Pottymania is when you start drawing Potty figures on scraps of paper or tracing Potty people in the sand on the beach. (That's a *really* bad sign.)

And of course, the final symptoms are restlessness and a feeling of unhappiness unless you are watching a Potty episode on television, or reading a Potty story. Naturally, this only happens if you become an absolute addict.

The Cure. Well, no one's found one yet. It's no good going to your doctor — he's probably as Potty as you are — so just give in and let it happen and make the best of it. After all, there's lots worse things than going Potty! I've been Potty for years!

Michael Bentine.

THE CASE OF THE POTTY HOUND OF THE BASKERVILLES

Sherlock 'Potty' Holmes and his friend Doctor Watson are two of the most famous Potty detectives in the whole history of crime and detection. From their house in Baker Street, London, they were called upon again and again when all else had failed and the best brains in the country were defeated, to foil the wicked schemes of that arch-Potty Plotter and international villain, Potty Professor Moriarty.

You see, the trouble was that Moriarty was a master of disguise and could turn himself into practically any other Potty in the twinkling of an eye. This made things very difficult for the Potty Scotland Yard detectives, because as soon as they had a description of the criminal, Moriarty would quick as a wink change his appearance, and completely flummox them. And so they frequently had to call in 'Potty' Holmes and Doctor Watson to help them solve the most baffling and dangerous cases, such as 'The Case of the Phantom Double Parker' and 'The Missing Rice Puddings'.

One of the detective's most famous cases was 'The Potty Hound of the Baskervilles', which nearly cost the life of one of Britain's most aristocratic aristocrats, Sir Hugo Baskerville, Bart. (That means Baronet, whatever *that* means.)

Sir Hugo came to see 'Potty' Holmes at his chambers in Baker Street (or was it his baker's in Chamber Street?); anyway, he turned up one day

looking pale and frightened, and told the great detective that he'd received a very threatening letter from someone who signed himself 'Anonymous'. This letter said (well, it didn't acually *say* anything —

unless you read it out loud) that Sir Hugo would be attacked by a great Hound which had been specially trained to attack people by the name of Baskerville (that's why it was called the Hound of the Baskervilles) UNLESS Sir Hugo paid an enormous sum of money — such as the whole contents of the Baskerville Piggy Bank. The letter went on to say that the ferocious Hound would bite the seat of his trousers off — which was why poor Sir Hugo was so afraid. After all, he didn't want to lose his country seat to anyone, let alone a Hound.

'Potty' Holmes settled his tweedy checked cape more comfortably around him, and sat back thoughtfully in his chair. He lit his pipe and blew a few careless smoke rings, then began to play his violin, while Sir Hugo waited patiently, hoping that the detective would stop smoking and violin-playing, neither of which things Sir Hugo liked at the best of times.

Suddenly 'Potty' Holmes stopped smoking his violin and playing his pipe (they'd somehow got a bit mixed up under his chin). He sat bolt upright and told Sir Hugo he had a plan...

The very next day they all went down to Baskerville hall — for two reasons: one, to carry out 'Potty' Holmes's plan, and the other because it was a nice sunny day and the Baskerville Hall strawberries were ripe. For two days they sat in the garden and ate strawberries till they couldn't stand the sight of them — and then suddenly they heard it! The sound of the Hound! WOW! It made your strawberries and cream curdle to hear it. Horrible, it was.

'Ah ha,' said 'Potty' Holmes calmly. 'Watson! My pistol and the packet of Dog Biscuits, please.'

Doctor Watson, always prepared, handed 'Potty' Holmes the pistol and Dog Biscuits.

'Well done, Watson!' cried Holmes, scattering the Dog Biscuits over the lawn.

At that moment the Hound of the Baskervilles loped into view. It was absolutely gigantic. It sniffed the Dog Biscuits, then, turning away from them, it wrinkled its nose, curled its lips back from its terrible teeth, and snarled menacingly.

'Ho ho!' remarked 'Potty' Holmes, without a trace of fear. 'Hands up — or rather, paws up, *Moriarty.*'

The Hound of the Baskervilles looked surprised, then threw up its front paws and, of course, fell flat on its tail.

Quick as a flash 'Potty' Holmes snapped hand-cuffs — or rather, paw-cuffs, on the Hound — or rather, on Moriarty.

'How on earth did you know that the Hound was Moriarty in disguise?' gasped Sir Hugo in amazement.

'Simple,' explained 'Potty' Holmes modestly. 'You see, the television advertisements guarantee that these Dog Biscuits are irresistible to any dog. And the Hound of the Baskervilles, being Moriarty and not a real dog, ignored them.'

'Amazing,' said Doctor Watson admiringly.

'Elementary, my dear Watson,' replied 'Potty' Holmes, idly nibbling a Dog Biscuit. 'Oh, I say, Watson,' he continued enthusiastically, 'do try these — they're really jolly good and they make a nice change from strawberries.'

A Potty Dotty Picture

Starting at number 1 and working in numerical order, join up the dots to make a Potty picture!

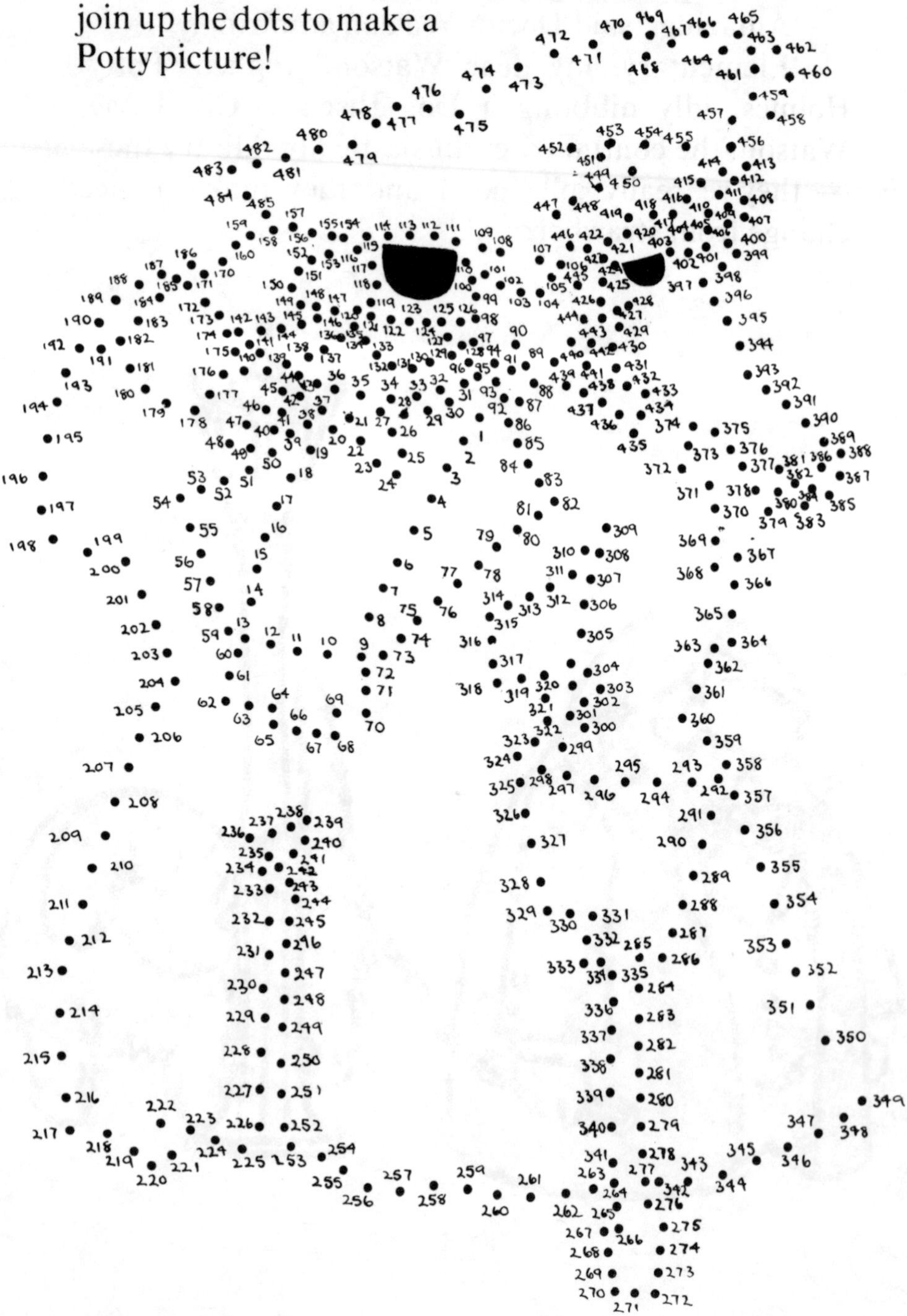

Pirate Buses

We've all heard about pirates, with their pieces of eight and their pistols, their parrots and their pirate ships; we all know about their activities on the Spanish Main, capturing gold and burying it on desert islands. So you can imagine my surprise when I read in a newspaper about pirate *buses* on the South Coast. Well, you could have knocked me down with a Potty parrot plume. *Pirate buses?* On the *South Coast?* I went down to Brighton straight away to find out what it was all about from a Corporation Bus Company.

'Pirate buses! Pirate buses!' exploded an angry little Potty Bus Inspector. 'They're about all right, mate! And they're taking our passengers away from us, too. I should say we're worried — here we are, a South Coast Corporation Bus Company, giving the public a nice, safe, kindly and efficient service for years, and along comes one of these jumped-up, good-for-nothing piratical bus companies and starts capturing *our* passengers. Wicked and piratical, I call it, mate!' And he was so angry that he had to disappear into the bus depot snack bar for a quick glass of lemonade and a soothing hot meat pie.

Obviously there really *were* pirate buses about the South Coast. But why *pirate* buses, I asked myself. As usually happens when I ask myself a question I can't answer, I didn't get a reply — so I set off along the coast road to try to find a pirate bus. It wasn't long before, rounding a bend in the road, I suddenly came across one standing at a bus stop. It was a pirate bus, all right — I could tell by the brass cannons gleaming on the top deck and the Jolly Roger (the pirate flag) flying from a short pole at the back.

'Ho ho, matey! Coming for a trip with us?' cried a gruff voice, and a Potty figure looking exactly like Long John Silver, complete with parrot, climbed out of the cab.

'That's right, matey,' said the pirate, noticing my astonishment, 'Long John Silver they calls me on the pirate buses — 'cos I only takes silver from 'em — I won't take notes — and if they 'aven't got silver, I makes 'em walk the plank. Ah ha!' He cackled gleefully.

'Walk the plank?' I repeated, aghast.

'That's our piratical bus talk for slinging 'em off

the bus, matey. And now I suppose you want to know what a pirate bus is. Well now, we pirate buses are what they call Free Enterprise Buses — we don't operate like the Corporation Buses — we're free souls and we run the old bus 'cos we enjoy it, see — and we charge what we like, matey. Ho ho! Ha ha! A life on the rolling main road for us, Jim lad!'

'My name's Michael,' I said timidly.

'Well then, Mike lad! Ha ha! Now, stand aside, ye land lubber, 'cos we're off on a Piratical Bus run, and this time we're armed!' Long John pointed up at the top deck where the cannons gleamed wickedly in the sunshine. 'And if it comes to a showdown with the Corporation Buses — well, may the best bus win. Avast there, me hearties, ahoy, and other nautical-piratical expressions.'

Long John adjusted the parrot on his shoulder, and hopped on his one leg over to his bus. I 'hopped it' too — straight back to the Corporation Bus Depot. Not that I wanted to sneak on Long John Silver, but I did want to find out what would happen next.

The Bus Inspector, Mr Bloggs, was not at all surprised when I told him about the pirate bus I'd seen.

'Let 'em all come,' he shouted bravely. 'We're ready for 'em.' He turned and called into the darkness of the bus shed. 'Braithwaite! Bring out Number Seven!'

'Aye aye!' a distant voice yelled back, and with a muttering roar a newly-painted Corporation Battle-bus emerged, cannons shining, Union Jack proudly flying, manned by a smartly-uniformed Corporation Bus crew.

'What a sight, eh?' Mr Bloggs beamed with pride.

'There's nothing to beat a fine, well turned-out bus of the line!'

He then performed the age-old ceremony of handing over to the conductor his ticket-issuing machine and fifty pence in change. This ritual over, Mr Bloggs saluted, shook the conductor warmly by the hand, and waved the bus off. With a ting-ting of its bell, it drove off into the sunset.

Suddenly, round the corner of the High Street lurched the Pirate Bus! Its crew hung out of the windows, shouting murderous Piratical Bus oaths like 'No more room on top!' and 'There's another one behind!' And Long John's villainous parrot was clinging on to the wing mirror screeching 'Any more fares, please?' in a most unpleasant way.

Immediately all was confusion on board the two buses as they slowly approached each other, preparing for action. Tickets were hurriedly punched and

passengers were slung off (rather rudely, I'm afraid). Then, as they drew alongside each other — Bang Bang Bang! went the cannons, loaded to the muzzle with old bus tickets, Irish pennies and aniseed balls.

What a sight it was, as bits of old advertisements were torn off the sides of the buses by the blasts. The bus crews lost their caps and their leather change bags were ripped open, showering coins of all descriptions over the road.

Twice the buses passed each other, firing broadsides, then, turning round the roundabouts at opposite ends of the High Street, they thundered down on each other to do battle again. This furious fighting couldn't last — suddenly the Pirate Bus skidded and came to a halt with steam hissing from its radiator. Its fan belt had bust in the heat of battle. Three hearty cheers rang out from the Corporation Bus, and it was all over.

'What will you do with the Pirates?' I asked Mr Bloggs as he wiped his smoke-stained, weary brow.

'Do with 'em? Do with 'em?' repeated Mr Bloggs, somewhat repetitively. 'We'll maroon 'em, of course — chain 'em to a Corporation Request Bus Stop. Yes, mate, I thought that would surprise you! But that'll teach 'em a lesson — you see, no self-respecting Corporation Bus *ever* stops at a Request Stop!'

Cor, what a fiendish idea, I thought as I mounted my trusty bicycle and pedalled back to London. No more buses for me — at least, not until I get a puncture!

Potty Sports Round-up

Just like everyone else, Pottys love sport. But of course their sports are just that little bit different, because after all, they are *Potty*. For example, take their favourite game, football. In the considered opinion of Potty football fans, the world's greatest Potty experts on the game — and consequently the greatest players — are the Worms. That is to say, the Worms that live in football grounds. Well, it stands to reason, doesn't it — they get a Worm's-eye view of the world's best players in action, so they *must* know all there is to know about it.

Worm Football — or rather, Worm Headball (for Worms don't have feet; instead they have two heads — one at each end) is played seven Worms a side, which

gives each team fourteen heads. The Worms wear club colours and the goalkeepers wear cloth caps and striped jerseys. Naturally, there are also Potty Worm trainers, managers and referees. The same rules that we observe in football aply to Worm Football, except that in addition to half-time, there may also be sudden breaks in the game when the players disappear a little sharply because of the invasion of the pitch by spectators — that is to say, hungry birds.

For the same reason, Worm Football is never played early in the morning; it wouldn't do for the early bird to catch your star player and give him a permanent transfer.

Another great Potty sport is Snail Racing. The snail-racing season starts during the summer and takes place at well-known race courses around the country such as Aintree and Newmarket. and giant snails, bred specially for the purpose, are ridden by skilled Potty jockeys dressed in gay racing colours. Normally this form of snail racing is on the flat (that is to say, no jumps), because steeple-chasing (that is to say, with jumps) takes so long for the snails to climb over the obstacles in their path that everyone gets bored and goes home.

Fast Snail Racing and Grand Prix events take place at race tracks like Silverstone and are undertaken by the snails themselves. These specially fast snails (known as E-Types) wear crash helmets and fill up from fuel pumps containing high-performance

racing slime. This is a jolly fast and very exciting sport, and skids and pile-ups are all too frequent. Luckily, their shells are so strong that none of the Racing Snails ever gets hurt physically — though of course their pride tends to be a little injured if they lose.

And of course, one mustn't forget that grand old Potty sport, Mexican Snail-Fighting, which takes place in a snail-ring, or big arena. The snail-fighters, dressed in bright red capes, first stick banderillos — or gaily-coloured stickers — onto the shell of the snail. Then they whip off their capes and fight the snails with them. Incidentally, the Mexican fighting snail is one of the most ferocious fighting snails in the world, so it's quite a dangerous sport for the Potty toreadors.

Finally, two very popular Potty winter sports are Yeti Ski-Jumping and Slalom Racing. Apart from the obvious reason why you need plenty of snow for these two sports, there is the additional one of ensuring that the yetis don't melt in the sun. And of course, only fully-grown yetis take part, as the younger ones (or notyetis, as they're called) are too small and could become buried in the snow drifts.

A Potty Word Game

How many words of two or more letters can you make out of the word POTTYMANIA? If you can find more than seventy, I reckon you must be a Potty genius!

Answers on page 96

The Greatest World War One Aces

During the First World War the pilots who flew those early, primitive, rickety aeroplanes were called 'aces' if they were really the tip-top flyers. Aces on both sides of the War became world famous with their daring flying feats, and there's no denying the bravery and skill of those pilots in their little fighter planes, which were made mainly out of wood and fabric, with engines that weren't very reliable and quite frequently stopped altogether. Of course, all this was in the days when

people settled their differences by fighting each other around the skies, like dogs do around the streets. That's why those battles in the sky were called 'dogfights' — and they were just as fierce, too.

Naturally, there was great rivalry among the pilots to be the very best. Two of the greatest rival Potty aces were Captain ffanshawe and Baron von Spitfaster.

Many were the dogfights those two aces had been through, and both had reached the top of their profession, outdaring and outfighting all other pilots. After years of dropping small bombs on each other's airfields — or, as they were called then, aerodromes — and knocking the hangars down and machine gunning each other's washing as it hung on the clothes-line to dry, they met at last in 1918, right at the end of the War.

Flying high in the sky in their little machines, they

suddenly spotted each other — and went into the attack. How they roared round and round up in the blue, while their machine guns barked like Potty puppies! They were jolly good pilots all right, but pretty rotten shots, and eventually they both had to come down to the ground because they'd run out of petrol. Before they could attack each other again, the War was over.

Today these two great rival aces live in retirement, crotchety and rheumatic and confined to Bath chairs, but still full of lively stories about their exploits in their famous planes — Captain ffanshawe's 'Spad' fighter plane, and Baron von Spitfaster's 'Fokker D Seven'.

What tales of twisting, turning, zooming dogfights they told me when I visited them at ffanshawe Hall,

where Baron von Spitfaster was guest of honour. Although they were the greatest rivals, they now visit each other once a year, their enmity forgotten as they recall glorious old deeds of derring-do, while their faithful old wartime mechanics, Corporal Braithwaite and Corporal Ulrich, look after them still.

As they sat on the lawn in their Bath chairs, how they argued endlessly about who was the better pilot! Both of them claimed that the other was the ace of

aces; each irritably maintained that the other had been more daring and more skilful. They began to thump their Bath chairs angrily as they struggled to remember dim facts to settle the argument. Then they started to wave their arms about and brandish their lemonade glasses, while their voices rose higher and higher and grew louder and louder.

Suddenly, Captain ffanshawe's temper gave way completely and he propelled his Bath chair straight at Baron von Spitfaster. The Baron hastily retreated, putting his Bath chair into reverse gear and retiring behind a large rose-bush, while Captain ffanshawe circled round and round, looking for a chance to catch the Baron off his guard and pepper him with the toy machine gun he had fixed to his Bath chair. But the Baron broke away, zigzagging across the lawn, and returning the Captain's fire before diving for cover under the cedar tree.

Round and round the garden they went, and when they'd run out of steam and could no longer manoeuvre the Bath chairs themselves, the faithful

Corporals Braithwaite and Ulrich pushed them. I've never seen such a Potty sight as those two ancient flying aces hurtling around the flower-beds, stopping every now and then for a reviving glass of lemonade, and then continuing the chase, puffing and blowing, red in the face, and pretending to shoot each other with their toy machine guns. They were still at it when I left, with the sun going down behind the oak trees of ffanshawe Park. What a good thing they're really such harmless old Pottys!

The Farmers And The Moles

An Every Day Story Of Country Pottys

I must say, I'd always rather liked the idea of farming as a career — until I met two very worried Potty farmers, who were at their wit's end because of the havoc caused to their vegetable crops by marauding moles.

'Nurdlums, they are,' grated Hezekiah through clenched teeth, 'nukky nigh noo nurdlums.'

'Ah, that they be,' agreed his brother Obadiah. 'Nukky nigh noo nurdling nigglums, they moles be. They creeps under the earth and tugs at the veg. from underneath, the little nurdlums. Whoosh! Whoosh! They plants disappears before your very eyes.'

The problem sounded serious. When I talked to

them, the brothers were waiting for the Ministry of Agriculture and Fisheries to send down an expert in de-moling mole-ridden farms like theirs, and I was lucky enough to meet the great man himself. He was the actual Permanent Under-Under-Secretary to the Permanent Under-Secretary! We all felt deeply honoured by the visit of so distinguished a man, and he graciously acknowledged our humble greeting as we bowed our heads and touched our forelocks (that is to say, the bit of hair at the front of our heads which from time immemorial — or even earlier — we ordinary folk have been expected to touch as a sign of respect to our betters). The Permanent Under-Etc. wasted no time in getting on with the job.

'There's been a right plague of them, this Spring,' he said gravely. 'Have they gone after your carrots much?'

'Whole fields of our lovely carrots bin masticated into 'orrible little lumps,' muttered Hezekiah bitterly. 'I'd give half my mangel-wurzels to see the last of them nukky nigh noo nurdlums.'

'I beg your pardon?' said the Permanent Under-Etc. faintly, not sure that he'd heard aright.

'Nukky nigh noo nurdlums—them moles. Nukky nigh nigglums, they be,' repeated Hezekiah, stabbing a stubby finger towards the moles' hideout.

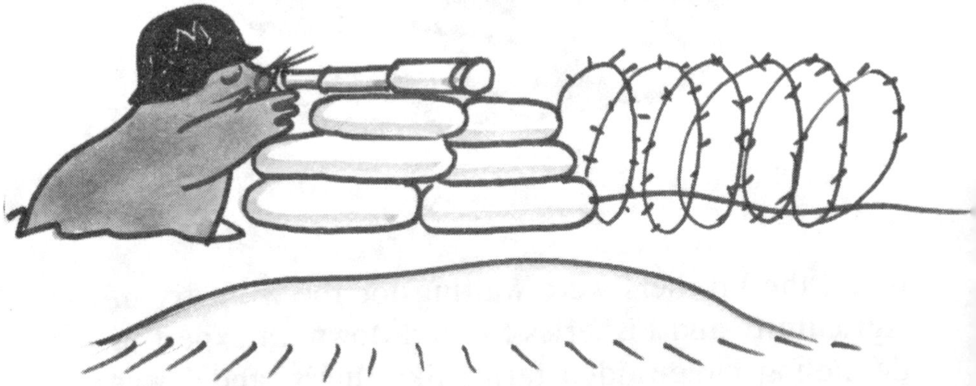

'Well, they won't be much longer,' said the Permanent Under-Etc. briskly. 'I'll sound the attack.' And from his waistcoat pocket he drew a whistle attached to a silver chain, and blew on it loudly. Immediately a ministry mortar team appeared and began to fire volley after volley of smoke shells towards the mole warren, stirring the occupants into a fever of black velvet activity, as the moles manned (or moled, I

suppose) their trenches. Coughing and choking, they reached for their gas-masks and continued their stubborn resistance.

'You see how it be?' remarked Obadiah despondently. 'There bain't nothing can shift they little nurdling nigglums.'

But the Permanent Under-Etc. hadn't finished. He ordered in a crop-spraying aircraft, flown by a ministry pilot, which roared over the moles' hideout spraying nasty dust to make the moles sneeze. But the moles just retaliated by eating almost a whole field of beetroot. Then an anti-mole tank rolled up, took aim, and pounded the mole-trenches with anti-mole shells. Great holes appeared in their barricades, and pretty soon the moles' defences were completely destroyed. This was too much for the moles, and coughing and sneezing, their little eyes watering, they surrendered in their thousands. Raising their little black muddy paws over their heads, they left their trenches while Hezekiah and Obadiah cheered heartily.

'What are you going to do with them?' I asked, feeling very sorry for the moles as they were rounded up and taken prisoner.

'Only one thing to do with these — what did you call them? — oh yes, nukky nigh noo niggling little nurdlums. That's to put them where they can't do any more harm — in our special mole prison. You must have heard of Moleditz?' replied the Permanent Under-Etc.

But later, as Obadiah and Hezekiah and I stood outside Moleditz Prison congratulating ourselves on having rid the farm of moles, ominous little bumps began appearing under the earth at our feet. It was the moles, escaping by tunnelling out of Moleditz! I left the two farmers 'nukky nigh noo nurdling and niggling' and scrambling about over the molehills which surrounded them. Farming may be a nice career, I thought, but at least in the town you don't have moles digging the ground from under your feet!

Extracts from Professor Pottsworthy's

ENCYCLOPÆDIA POTTANICA

Or, Great Pottys in History.

MARCO POLO. The world's best-known and first *commercial* traveller. Starting from Venice, his home-town, he took his goods — Italian tomato sauce, stinky Gorgonzola cheese and Chianti wine — all over Asia and the Far East, exchanging them for all sorts of things: curry powder and spices from India; Persian cats from Persia; lemon curd from Kurdistan; Afghan hounds from Afghanistan; and of course, spag-het — or, as it came to be known in Italy, 'spaghetti' — from China.

The Great Khan of China (not to be confused with his brother, the Great Khant, who wasn't much good at anything) invited Marco and his friend, little Giuseppe, who kept the accounts, to stay at his Imperial Palace in Peking.

Marco and Giuseppe enjoyed their stay immensely, except that they didn't get much sleep at night because of the yapping of the Pekingese dogs. They learnt how to make and

fly Chinese kites, and had great fun trying to eat with chopsticks. In exchange for Marco's tomato sauce, the Great Khan offered him fireworks and spag-het. Unfortunately he explained what to do with them in Chinese, which Marco didn't understand. However, cleverly figuring that you ate one and set fire to the other, he poured tomato sauce over the fireworks and lit the spag-het. The fireworks

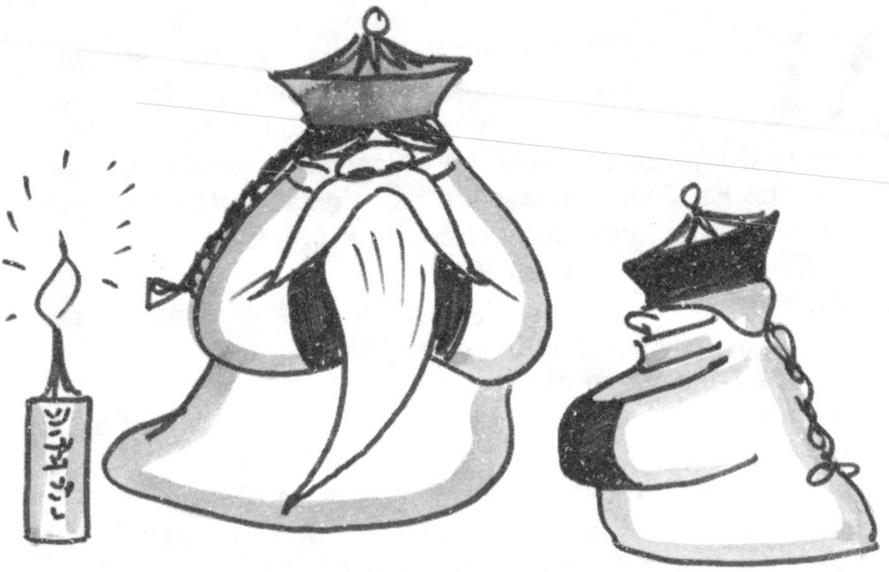

didn't taste very nice and the spag-het took ages to catch fire, but Marco took them back with him to Venice. There they soon realised that it was the other way round, and took to cooking spaghetti with as much care as they set light to the fireworks.

But what a sight met Marco's eyes on his return to Venice! He had left his bath taps running when he went away on his travels to China, and Venice was now flooded. Still, as Marco said to Giuseppe, 'It's gonna be a big attraction for the tourists.'

QUEEN ELIZABETH I. Popularly known as 'Good Queen Bess', she spent most of her life trying not to get married. This was because she was too busy ruling Elizabethan England, and going to 'first nights' of new plays by William Shakespeare, and running England's biggest business, which was waylaying Spanish galleons and taking off them the gold and silver that the Spaniards had stolen from the South American Indians, and — well, anyway, Queen Elizabeth was just *too* busy to get married. King Philip of Spain wanted very badly to marry her so that he could get back his gold and silver, but the Queen flatly refused him. 'Never in the history of England,' she announced, 'shall an Elizabeth marry a Philip.' In the end Philip became so furious that he built a huge fleet of ships, called the Armada, to invade England.

Luckily Sir Francis Drake and Sir Walter Raleigh were back from one of their 'business' trips (pinching the Spaniards' gold) and were able to stop the invasion. This made Philip madder than ever, and to get even he left instructions in his will that all English tourists holidaying on the Costa Brava should be charged double. (Of course, that was years later, but then, Philip was a very nasty King who always bore grudges.)

LEONARDO DA VINCI. Leonardo, who according to his name, came from Vinci (wherever that is — somewhere in Italy, I shouldn't wonder), was a very good painter. He started early as a boy — and you can't really start much earlier than that, unless of course you're a girl. He painted such Italian road signs as 'Goa Slowa!' and 'Keepa to da Lefta!' and so on. Then he began to paint signs on hilly roads (like 'Steepa Hilla!'), and the hills got steeper and steeper till he was painting vertically — or upright as it is called — on walls — things like 'Tommy go home!' and 'Fred loves Mabel!'

One day the Duke of Milan saw him doing one of his cartoons on a wall and got to him just before the police did, and hired him to be his own personal painter, to do portraits and pictures and signs like 'Don'ta painta on dese walls!'.

Leonardo became very famous and being a clever man, he decided he would have a side-line — that is to say, a trade by which he could make his living if he ever ran out of paint, or if people didn't want any more pictures or signs. So he invented tanks and flying machines and all sorts of machinery and egg-beaters and mousetraps and lemon-squeezers and heaven knows what — but he never seemed to make much money, until he had a brainwave and invented life insurance and insured himself for a fortune. He then died a very rich man.

HADRIAN. A well-known Roman general and wall-builder, Hadrian's most famous wall separates Scotland from England (or England from Scotland, depending on which side you're on), and was built entirely from bricks made by Hadrian's own brick-making company. He built the wall to keep back the Picts and the Scots, who would clan together and storm down through England,

throwing hammers and tossing cabers and putting shots and highland flinging, and generally running amok, causing untold damage. However, Hadrian's Wall put paid to that,

and once a year he would let them through so that they could rush down (in an orderly manner) to Londinium for the annual Scotland versus England football match.

The funny thing was that the Roman legionaries who guarded the wall began to speak with a Scottish accent — while the Pics and the Scots had picked up the Romans' Italian accent. All very confusing, but typically Potty.

KING ARTHUR. Everyone used to think of King Arthur and his famous Knights as dashing men in shining armour who led a leisurely life surrounded by beautiful damsels in fancy silks and satins with long pointed hats. But in fact King Arthur was the head of a band of working-class knights who worked their fingers to the bone killing off dragons, rescuing young ladies and foiling ogres. Overworked and underpaid (just like most of us today), King Arthur and his knights eventually became fed up with their 'knightly' working conditions and formed themselves into a Union — or 'Knights of the Round Table' as they called themselves. King Arthur was elected shop-steward, and he called all the distressed damsels and fiery dragons and

wicked ogres to a meeting and told them bluntly that his Knights were not working more than a 40-hour week rescuing and slaying and foiling, and that Sundays and weekends would be double-overtime, and if they didn't like it the Knights would go on strike and have a sit-in round their Round Table, and all the distressed damsels, dragons and unfoiled ogres could jolly well go and jump in the lake!

Naturally there was a big row and the Knights picketed Camelot, which was where they worked, and beat up errant knights who tried to break the strike, and oh, there was a heck of a to-do! In the end the damsels and dragons and ogres grew tired of being distressed, unslain and unfoiled and agreed to King Arthur's terms and everyone lived happily ever after — or at least, until the next election.

A Visit To The Army Cookery Corps

I've always thought that life in the army must be very exciting and adventurous, so I was especially pleased when (as Roving Reporter for 'Potty Time') I was sent to find out about the Army Cookery Corps (not to be confused with the Army Catering Corps).

I must say that when I met the Colonel of the Corps I was very impressed—firstly, he looked so splendid in his bearskin (note: *not* bare skin) and regimental uniform; and secondly, he had a lovely smell about him — a mixture of roast and two veg., Yorkshire pudding and jam rolypoly.

As he marched towards me and halted smartly, he was followed by his Sergeant Major, a rather smaller Potty, who was also very smartly turned out, and smelt of roast lamb and mint sauce. Behind *him* came a Corporal (smelling of fried eggs and bacon) and two Privates (wafting the delightful aroma of cottage pie and custard*).

'Allow me to introduce myself,' said the Colonel, politely offering me his right hand, in which he held a ham sandwich. I took the ham sandwich and shook the hand. I remember he had a good firm handshake and it was a jolly good firm ham sandwich.

'I'm Colonel Suet,' he continued, 'Commander-in-Chef of the Army Cookery Corps.'

'Delighted to meet you,' I replied, between munches of the excellent ham sandwich. 'I'm reporting for 'Potty Time' — name's Bentine.'

'No relation to 'Nosher' Bentine of the 18th Light Infantry, by any chance?' asked the Colonel. 'He was very partial to ham sandwiches, too.'

'Possibly a distant cousin,' I said. 'Now, tell me, Colonel, is it true what they say about army food? That it's not as good as civilian cookery?'

'What!' exploded Colonel Suet, turning red in the face like a turkey (or a perfectly-cooked lobster). 'What! Did you hear that, lads?'

The lads had heard, and were making furious

* Of course, I don't mean they smelt of cottage pie *with* custard — only that *one* smelt of cottage pie and the *other* of custard.

sounds and gestures to show that they had.

'What an insult to a great regiment!' cried the Sergeant, and the whiskers of his moustache, still green with the mint sauce he had been tasting, bristled with rage. 'Cor, stone Mrs Beeton's crow pie!'

'Of course it's not true,' said Colonel Suet. 'The Cookery Corps has produced the finest food in the world for the finest troops in the world, from the time of Waterloo, when Napoleon Whatsisname said the British Army marched on its stomach, to El Alamein and the Desert Rats' favourite meat and veg. The Cookery Corps provided meals that made the British troops get up and go — sometimes twice a day — to capture the German food dumps. Well, just let me tell you, sir, the Cookery Corps flag has flown proudly, though fired at by shot and shell, rissole and meat pie.'

'Just think of this menu for a moment,' the Sergeant Major broke in enthusiastically. 'Caviar, champagne, fillet steak and mushrooms, saute potatoes, ice cream and chocolate sauce, and Irish coffee to follow!'

'Good heavens! Do the troops eat that?' I asked, amazed, wondering where I could volunteer to join up.

'No,' replied the Sergeant Major, 'but just think of it!'

A full minute's solemn silence followed while we all thought reverently of it. Then the Colonel sighed and continued.

'Do you know that the British Army today has the finest cooking equipment in the world? And with the finest raw food materials in the world to match it, we can teach a first-class civilian truck mechanic to become an army cook almost as quickly as we can teach a first-class civilian cook to become an army truck mechanic! It's all in the Army Cookery Manual,' he went on proudly, slapping a large book which he carried under his arm.

'May I see that?' I asked hopefully.

'I'm afraid not,' replied the Colonel sternly. 'You see, it's top secret and heaven knows what the enemy —' He dropped his voice and looked furtively over his shoulder. '—what the enemy would give,' he went on, 'to lay their grubby hands on our new secret recipe for super-dumplings — or, as they're called by their code name, "Sinkers". Oh, no, I'm afraid you can't see inside this magnificent document — it's the sum total of two hundred years of slaving over hot stoves by the great army cooks of the past.'

At that, the Sergeant Major and his troops saluted proudly and one of the Privates blew a long, piercing call through a piece of macaroni. To put it in a nutshell

(walnut, officers, for the use of), the British Army Cookery Corps today stands where it has always stood — proudly — boldly — and covered in cold gravy.

'Look at Private Haddock there,' said the Colonel. 'Typical army cook, Haddock is. Decorated twice for bravery and once for rice pudding. Notice his wooden spoon — so clean you could almost eat off it. Observe those hand grenades — empty, actually, and used as pepper and salt containers; note the mixed herbs in his tin helmet — for camouflage and flavouring, and his special army-pack pastry board — light short-crust pastry, for the rolling of. Now tell me you're not proud to be British.'

'Actually, I'm half British and half Peruvian,' I said.

'Oh, all right then,' replied the Colonel. 'Be half proud and half Peruvian.'

'It sounds a good safe job to be in,' I continued.

'Safe! Did you say *safe?* Did he say *safe,* Sergeant Major?' Colonel Suet could hardly believe his ears.

'He did, sir!' said the Sergeant Major. 'He said safe, sir.'

'Great Spotted Dick!' spluttered the Colonel. 'Being a cook is the most dangerous job in the whole army! One false move while seasoning the stew, and the unfortunate army cook could find himself covered from head to foot in Brown Windsor Soup. They're very particular, the troops, you know.'

'My apologies, sir,' I said humbly.

'No offence taken,' said the Colonel kindly. 'Otherwise I'd have had you boiled in parsley sauce! Well, you'll have to forgive me now — I'm off to inspect the cookhouse, Right, lads — on with your gas masks and forward march!!!'

The Great Potty Snail Race

1 Trace the Potty snails onto thin card (four plain postcards are ideal).
2 Fold each card in half along the dotted line, so that the snail stands up on its own. You'll notice that each snail has a different symbol on its shell — that is to say, a heart, a diamond, a club or a spade — corresponding to the four suits in a pack of cards.
3 Now take a pack of cards and lay out 13 cards in a row, face downwards. Then put this pack away and line up your four snails at one end of the row.
4 Next, take a second pack of cards, remove the jokers, shuffle, and turn up each card in turn as though you're playing 'Snap'. Whatever the first card is that you turn up (whether heart, diamond, club or spade), move the corresponding snail one card along the row. Then turn up the next card, and move whichever snail corresponds to that, and so on. The first snail to reach the thirteenth card in the row is the winner!

Note 1: If you've only got one pack of cards, you can draw the thirteen squares of the race course on a piece of paper.
Note 2: If you want a longer game, you can lay out 26 cards in a row, but you'll have to shuffle the second pack of cards when the first snail gets to the thirteenth card.

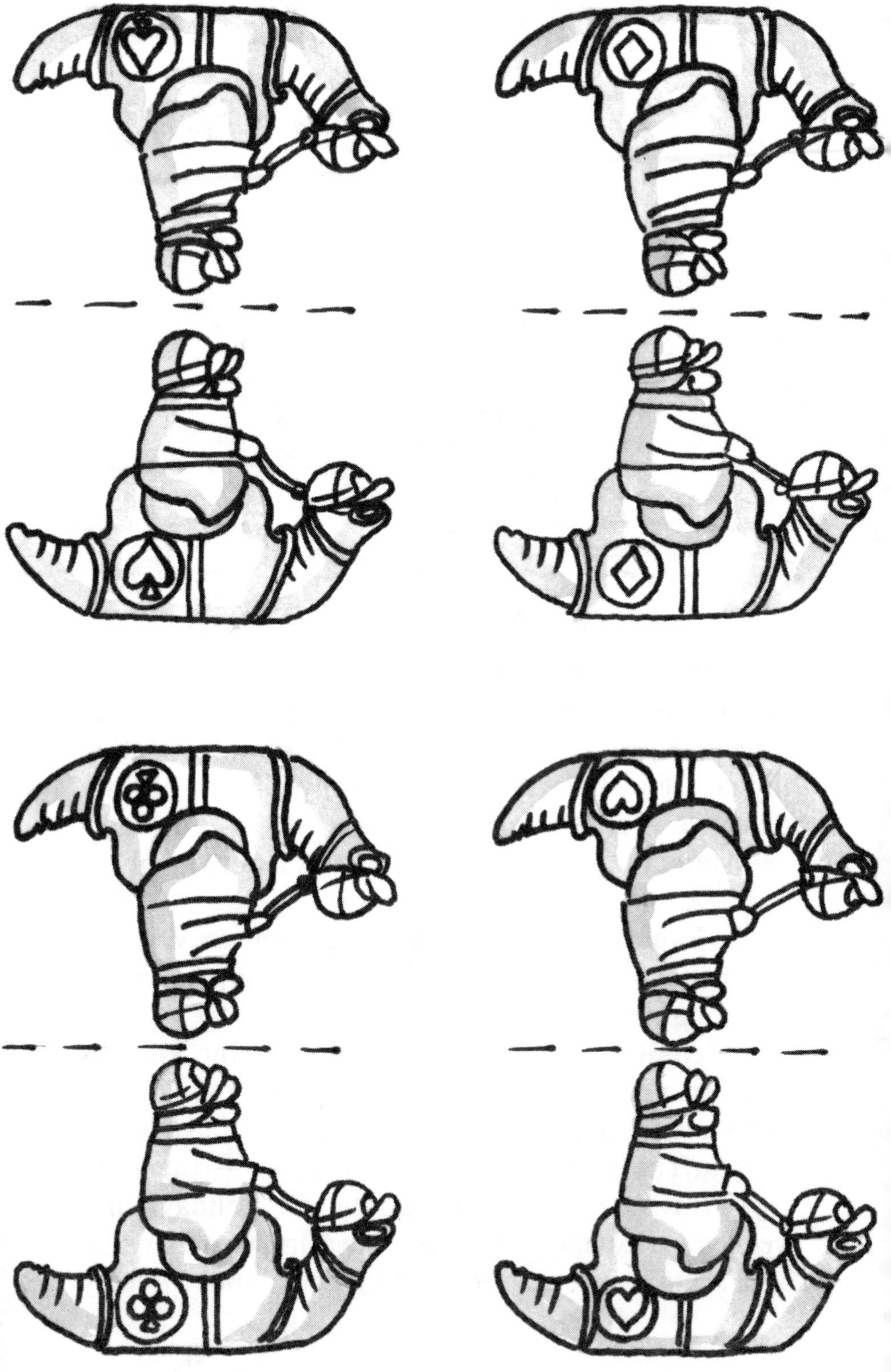

The Missing Hire Cruisers Mystery

I'd seen vague reports in the newspapers about hire cruisers on the River Thames disappearing without trace, and I thought I'd do a bit of investigation myself. Now, I've always fancied myself as a bit of a detective — always carry a spyglass, just in case, and a deerstalker hat — just in case there's a deer involved. Can't be too careful, you know.

So I went down to the Thames Conservancy, which looks after and preserves the River Thames, and made a few enquiries.

'Well, it's supposed to be top secret,' the Thames Conservancy Potty (T.C.P. for short) told me cautiously, 'but seeing as how you seem to have heard Certain Things, I'll tell you. Hire cruisers — that is to say, cruisers hired by the public for holidays and weekend trips and such, have been mysteriously disappearing between Teddington Lock and Molesey

Lock — disappearing from the face of the river!' he said dramatically.

'Now,' he went on, 'these missing hire cruisers are causing quite a stir. After all, you can't have all these families just vanishing — people are beginning to ask awkward questions. It's getting very embarrassing.'

'Well, what are you doing about it?' I asked.

'Aha! We're not fools in the Conservancy, you know — we've got our plans.' He tapped the side of his nose significantly and looked round to see that he wasn't being overheard. 'For instance, there's Conservancy Riverman Butterworth. Butterworth!' he suddenly shouted, cupping his hands to make his voice carry over the peaceful surface of the river.

'Aye aye, sir!' The voice seemed to be coming from a dense bank of reeds. These were suddenly thrust aside, and out swam the largest, whitest swan I've ever seen. With a rustling of feathers, a muffled sneeze and a grunt, the head and shoulders of a brawny Potty riverman appeared out of the swan's back.

'That's Butterworth,' said the T.C.P. proudly. 'He's on the look-out.'

'For what?' I asked.

'For anything worth looking out for,' replied the T.C.P., a little testily. 'Then there's Wilkins. Wilkins!' he yelled towards the other side of the river.

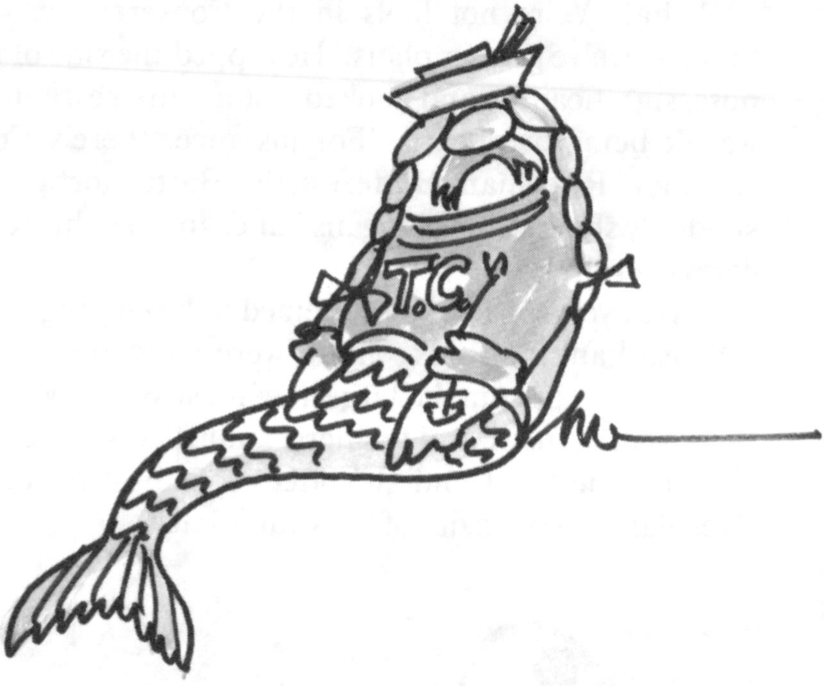

From under the branches of a thick weeping willow came a strange-looking figure. It shuffled along on its bottom and as it came nearer I could see that the top half of it was another Thames Conservancy River Potty, wearing a glamorous long blonde wig. His bottom half was encased in a mermaid's tail. No wonder he couldn't walk properly — he was like a fish out of water!

'Rubber,' said the T.C.P. with pride, following my

startled glance. 'Made Wilkins's fishy bottom half meself, out of foam rubber.'

'But why—what's he doing?' I asked, bewildered.

'Wilkins,' replied the T.C.P., 'is a trap. You've heard of sirens—those lovely ladies who lure sailors to their doom? Well, he's trying to entice into our trap whatever it is that's swiping our hire cruisers. I'll show you.'

The T.C.P. blew his Bosun's Pipe * loudly and, with an answering blast, a Thames pleasure boat hove into view round the bend of the river. At the tiller sat an old riverman, and its only passenger was a large fat nursemaid with a pram.

'That's the trap,' said the T.C.P., happily nodding his head. 'You see that pram? Well, inside it there's a small cannon. As for the nursemaid, that's Fred, our master gunner. They look peaceable enough as they cruise along, but my bet is that between 'em they'll lure the villains, whoever they are, to destruction.'

There didn't seem to be much scope for my detective abilities, I thought despondently. It all seemed to be under control. Suddenly, as I was about to lob my deerstalker out into the river—

'Look there! By the weir pool! Something's happening!' cried the T.C.P.

An eerie sight met my eyes. From out of the deep, dark, dangerous, whirling waters of the weir pool came a bubbling white froth, and a sinister submarine, rusty red with age, silently slipped up from the surface of the water. Its conning tower bore the number U1.

*A pipe used by Bosuns for blowing, not sucking — therefore no good for smoking.

'Good Queen Bessie's rowlocks!' shouted the T.C.P., using an ancient Thames Conservancy oath. All was panic stations. The pleasure boat unmasked its gun, and Fred the nursemaid threw off the pram cover to reveal the cannon, as the submarine's conning tower opened and a very aged Potty emerged, dressed immaculately in the uniform of a German captain.

'Halt der Boot!' he shouted in a cracked voice, 'or I vill sink you yet already!'

'Never!' yelled back the gallant crew of the pleasure boat, and opened fire.

The rusty old U-boat was no match for the trim, well-manned pleasure boat, not to mention a Thames Conservancy gunner trained to knock over poaching fishermen at five hundred yards. The very first shot carried away the U-boat's conning tower, and the second tore a large hole in its stern. It was all over in a few minutes. The old German U-boat captain wept with range and injured pride.

'I surrender, Kamerad,' he wheezed as he was

pulled, dripping, from the river. 'You haf won der war! Hans, take down der Kaiser's picture.'

By Jove! He was a World War One one (I mean, he was one from World War One, which we won!). And then the whole story came out. Over a hot cup of tea, and wrapped inj a warm blanket, Kapitan Dumkopf of the Imperial German Navy told all.

He had been sailing up and down under the Thames since 1918, and didn't know that the war had ended. Instead, he had gone on sinking and capturing hire cruisers and pleasure boats all those years. The missing boats were being held prisoner in a secret marina up-river — there are so many marinas being built on the Thames that nobody had ever noticed this one.

The hire cruiser families were all rescued, and everyone was happy — after all, they'd had a nice long extra holiday aboard the cruisers. Only the owners of the boats were a little grumpy. When they'd shouted 'Come in, Number Fourteen, your time is up!' no boat had appeared. And they couldn't really under the circumstances charge extra money for the extra time the cruisers had been out on the river.

Oh, well, they're all stark raving Potty if you ask me. And to think I didn't get to use my spyglass or my deerstalker *once.*

Directions for Making A Potty Easter Egg

very hard-boiled egg

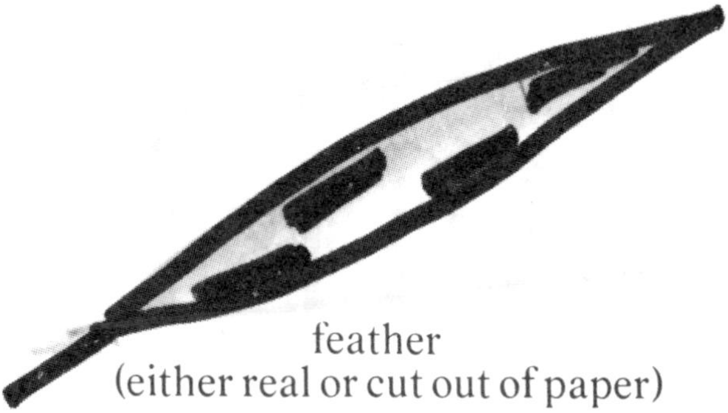

feather
(either real or cut out of paper)

arms cut out of stiff paper
and glued onto cone

cone of stiff paper
(cut cone from a semi-circle and colour it)

any Potty character
you like!

The Vikings

When I was a boy, I used to go for picnics near Walmer and Deal on the lovely Kent Coast, a part of the country that is full of interesting historical remains such as Roman forts and Ancient Britons' villages. It's where Julius Caesar landed during his invasion of Britain, and later, after the Romans had left, where the Viking dragon ships * raided the coastal villages.

*They were called dragon ships because they had a wooden dragon on the prow, *not* because, as some Potty twit has suggested, they were always 'draggin' 'em up the beach'.

On a recent visit to Walmer Beach on a blustery winter's day, I was amazed to bump into a Potty dressed in a long, flowing white robe, with hair down to his shoulders. He was a Druid — that is to say, an Ancient British Potty priest.

'Hello,' he said, prodding me with his sacred mistletoe branch. 'What's a giant like you doing here in these parts? We could certainly use you to help us against the Vikings. They're due here on Saturday and our full-back isn't fit for the match.'

I looked confused, as I always do when an enthusiastic Potty suddenly appears, talking nineteen to the Potty dozen.

'What Viking match?' I naturally asked.

'*The* Viking match,' replied the Druid. 'Really,' he muttered into his beard, 'these giants aren't too bright — all brawn and no brain. *The* Viking match, Big One.'

It seemed that the Vikings came every Saturday during the season and attacked the Ancient Britons' village — and the home team rushed out to defend their ground. Rather like football in a way.

The first line of defence was Fred, the early warning system, wearing specially large artificial ears — like headphones on a hi-fi stereo set. Fred would listen hard through a kind of trumpet and then, if he heard the Viking ships approaching (they made quite a racket, of course, what with all those oars), he would blow the great Potty warning horn.

Immediately the second line of defence — Bert, the fiercest Ancient Briton on that part of the coast — would hurl himself into action.

'Two-club Bert, we call him,' said the Druid proudly.

'How can he belong to *two* clubs?' I asked, puzzled.

'No, no, *no*!' cried the Druid. 'He doesn't *belong* to two clubs — he *uses* two clubs, one in each hand. Oh, he's a lovely clubber, is Bert.'

What a battle it must have been. All the Ancient Britons for miles around would pay almost any price — even as much as four dozen duck eggs, or a pound of best blue woad * — for a seat on the cliffs to watch the fight.

Bert would rush in and a real ding-dong-punch-up (or rather, club-up) would take place. Viking shields were beaten like a set of drums in a pop group. Then, if the Vikings fought their way past Bert, the Druid had a special line of defence. This was a very unusual

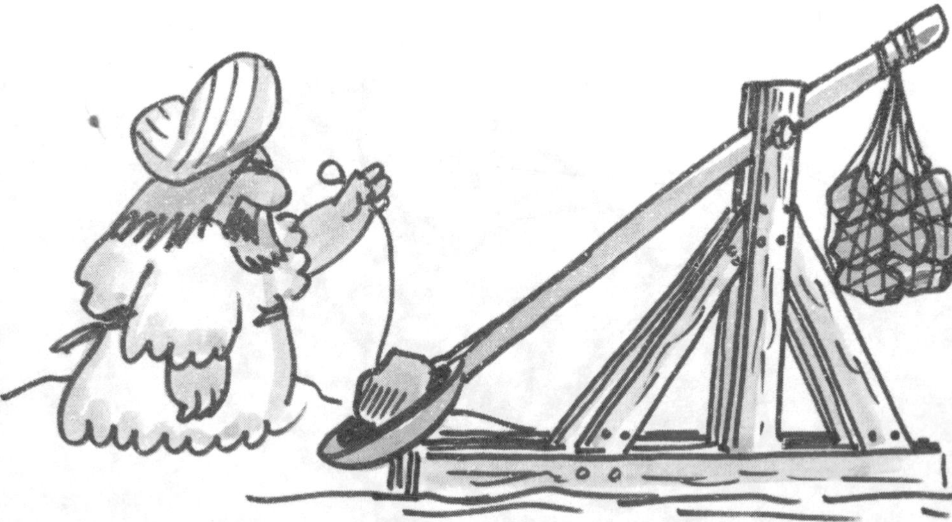

* In those days, instead of money they used a system of exchanging goods (known as barter), such as swapping a pair of socks for an old hat.

Ancient Briton who had been transferred from another part of the country at great cost — I believe the Druid mentioned the sum of three hundred pairs of second-hand sheepskin undervests!

'Transferred, he was,' said the Druid, 'from a northern club — Bradford City!' He paused dramatically and pointed to a small Ancient Briton in a turban who was oiling an enormous wooden catapult. As he worked, busily loading and testing his catapult, his turban bobbed merrily up and down and he hummed a lively little Northern tune.

'Best catapulter in the whole of Britain,' announced the Druid with great satisfaction, as the little Potty shot a beach rock clear across the sand and far out into the North Sea. I suppose it's this vague memory we present-day Britons have of heaving great stones at the Vikings that makes us want to throw pebbles out to sea as we walk along the beach.

The ancient Britons' final defence came as quite a surprise — even with all my experience of Pottys and the Potty way they think, I couldn't have guessed it. They used a *Customs Officer* to stop the Vikings if the catapult failed to deter them! There he was, in his Customs Officer's uniform, sternly holding a small

notice which said 'If you have anything to declare, stop here at Her Majesty's Customs'. (What Majesty, you may well ask? Why, Queen Boadicea herself, of course, who always attended at least one big Viking battle a year — usually the Viking Cup Final!) Well, the Ancient Potty Britons certainly had a good idea there, because no one, but *no one*, ever gets past a British Customs Officer without his express permission.

Next time you go down to the Kent Coast and walk along those beaches, think about the Vikings and the Ancient Britons — and who knows, you might just meet a Potty Druid or see a Potty Viking match!

A POTTY QUIZ
Or Twenty Potty Questions

OR, if you're the sort of Potty person who prefers to do things backwards, turn upside down to page 95 first, and make up twenty Potty Questions to fit the answers given there!

1 What is the Potty name for a mole?
2 Who left the bath tap running in Venice?
3 Why isn't Worm football ever played early in the morning?
4 When is a yeti a notyeti?
5 What happens when you ask yourself a question you can't answer?
6 Name the two greatest Potty World War I aces.
7 What is a Jolly Roger?
8 How many volumes are there in the Encyclopaedia Pottanica?
9 What did Marco Polo bring back from China?
10 How many are there in a Potty dozen?
11 Name three Potty sports.
12 How tall is an average Potty?
13 What is a dogastrophe?
14 Is there a cure for Pottymania?
15 What musical instrument did Sherlock 'Potty' Holmes play?
16 How did Long John Silver get his name?
17 What is T.C.P. short for?
18 Who is the most famous Potty medical specialist?
19 Where do the Pottys go to school?
20 Which prison were the moles sent to?

HOW TO MAKE A POTTY THEATRE

You need a cardboard box about 14 inches long and 8-10 inches wide and about 8 inches deep, preferably with a solid piece of cardboard for the bottom. Turn the box upside down and glue it to a piece of cardboard of the same size. Then cut out the holes as shown in Figure 1.

Run two pieces of string from one side of the box to the other so that you can hang your scenery on them. Clip the bent-over piece of scenery onto the string with paper clips (see Figure 2).

The cyclorama is a piece of cardboard slightly larger than the back of the box. Glue this on, bending it into a roundish shape (see Figure 3). This gives you a background which you can paint light blue to give the effect of sky.

Trace the characters, the props (that is, the trees, rocks, jar) and the scenery onto card then colour them all and cut them out.

The sliders for the characters are made out of a length of wire with a cardboard platform (or 'tab') stuck on the end. You then fix your character onto the tab with a paper clip (see Figure 4).

You can even make a curtain for your theatre — a piece of cardboard sliding down through a slot at the top of the box works very well.

Figure 1

Figure 3

Figure 2

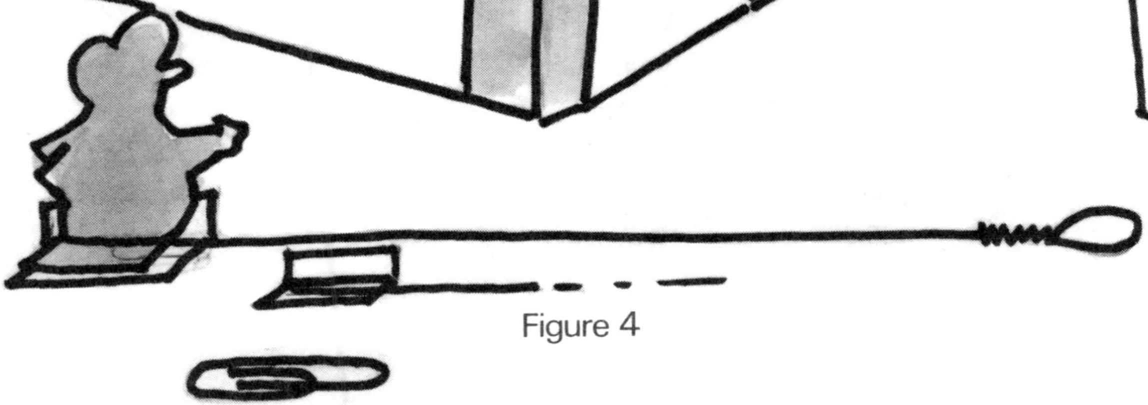

Figure 4

Sinbad the Sailor
A Potty Play

List of Characters

Sinbad the Sailor
Omar Khayyam, his friend
The Caliph of Baghdad
Sheherezade, his daughter
The Vizier, his adviser
The Roc — a gigantic bird
The Genie

Scene 1: A desert oasis outside Baghdad (use scenery and tree props)
Scene 2: Inside the Palace of the Caliph (use scenery and jar prop)
Scene 3: A wild, rocky part of the desert outside Baghdad (use cyclorama and rock props A and B)
Scene 4: Outside the Palace (cyclorama and Palace props C and D)

Scene 1: An oasis outside Baghdad. Enter Sinbad the Sailor and his friend, Omar Khayyam, on a flying carpet.

SINBAD — Omar, I've got a funny feeling that today I'm going to make my fortune.

OMAR — Well, we will never make any money from selling our flying carpets — they're too good — they never wear out.

SINBAD — Why not, Omar?

OMAR — Because they never touch the ground. No, we won't make a fortune that way. Maybe our hover-carpet taxi service will be a success.

SINBAD — Maybe, Omar my friend. But at the moment, everybody seems to prefer riding on camels. Anyway, let's try to find a rich passenger for our hover-carpet taxi. I know — we'll go to the Palace of the Caliph of Baghdad.

(They exit)

Scene 2: Inside the Palace of the Caliph. Change the scenery on the cross strings, and place the jar at the front of the stage. Enter the Caliph's daughter, Sheherezade, and Sinbad.

SINBAD — Excuse me, lovely lady. My name is Sinbad the Sailor. I rep-

	present the Sinbad-Omar hover-carpet taxi service. If you want to go anywhere, we can take you. Care to come for a drive?
SHEHEREZADE	Ooh, cheeky! I'll call my father, the Caliph. (*Calls*) Dad!

(Enter Caliph and Vizier)

CALIPH	You called, oh my daughter?
SHEHEREZADE	This fellow asked me to go for a drive with him on his hover-carpet.
CALIPH	You realise that this young lady is my daughter, the Princess Sheherezade?
SINBAD	Sorry, Your Majesty, I thought she was one of the Palace dancing-girls.
VIZIER	Your Majesty, perhaps this person is the one prophesied by the ancient prophet!
CALIPH	What is your name? Quickly now!
SINBAD	Sinbad the Sailor, Your Majesty.
CALIPH	Vizier, you could be right! The prophecy says one shall come from the sea and find the magic bottle, defeat the Giant Bird, the Great Roc, and marry the daughter of the Caliph.
SINBAD	Just give me a chance! Where is the magic bottle?
CALIPH	Somewhere in the great desert among the rocks. Find this

magic bottle and release the genie that is inside it, and you will be able to defeat the Terror of Baghdad — the Great Roc. Smash its egg, and the hand of my daughter, the lovely Sheherezade, shall be yours in marriage!

SINBAD — Trust the navy to have a go!

(They all exit)

Scene 3: A rocky part of the desert outside Baghdad. Put the two rock props on either side of the stage and use the cyclorama only at the back. Enter Sinbad and Omar. Sinbad carries a sword.

SINBAD — Hey, Omar, I can see something behind that rock. It's an old bottle!

(Sinbad goes behind one of the rocks and comes out with the bottle — slide them both out together)

OMAR — I don't know why you're getting so excited — it's just an old bottle.

SINBAD — I can hear something inside it. I'll open it behind this rock.

(Sinbad pushes the bottle back behind the rock, and reappears with the genie in the bottle)

SINBAD — Oh, genie, I am your master — Sinbad the Sailor.

GENIE — Oh, master, thank you a million times for releasing me from the bottle — I am your slave! Your wish is my command.

SINBAD	Why don't you come right out of the bottle?
GENIE	I can't — I'm too fat. You see, oh master, it's a ginger beer bottle and I've been drinking the ginger beer for a thousand years. Now I can only get my head outside — but I'm very grateful for that.
SINBAD	Where's the Giant Roc?
GENIE	Behind you, oh master.
SINBAD	No, no, genie — not R-O-C-K (*he spells it out*) but R-O-C — the Giant Bird.
GENIE	I told you, oh master — behind you.

(Slide in the Giant Roc's legs at the back)

ROC	Caw! Caw!
SINBAD	Cor! What do I do now, genie?
GENIE	Don't panic — I'll cast a spell. 'You who are so big and tall — Allez oops — now you are small!'

(Take out the Giant Roc's legs and substitute the Little Roc — which cheeps like a sparrow)

SINBAD	But where is the Roc's egg?
GENIE	Open Sesame!

(Pull back the other rock at the side of the stage — to reveal the egg)

GENIE	Open, Eggy!

(The egg comes apart in two halves and there is the Baby Roc making Baby Roc noises)

Scene 4: Outside the Caliph's Palace. Place the prop of the larger palace to one side at the back, and use the cyclorama behind it. The Caliph (the second version of him) and the Vizier are there; so are Sinbad and Sheherezade (the second picture of them, with the ring), Omar, and the Genie.

CALIPH — As I promised, you are now married to Sheherezade. Here is your palace!

SINBAD — Thank you a million times, oh Caliph — or should I say Dad? Come, my beautiful bride. To our Palace!

SHEHEREZADE — Ooh, you are awful — you sailors are all the same.

(They exit)

GENIE — Now Sinbad and his bride are
married —
On their honeymoon be carried!
Palace! Away you go on high —
I command you, Palace, fly!

(The Palace flies off, and then the smaller palace crosses the cyclorama — this second palace is on a piece of cotton so that you can dangle it through the slot at the top of the theatre.

CALIPH — Bye bye!

(He and the Vizier exit)

OMAR — And so they lived happily ever after!

(Omar exits on his flying carpet)

THE END

BEND
Sinbad
BEND
Sinbad

BEND
Sinbad
Sheherezade

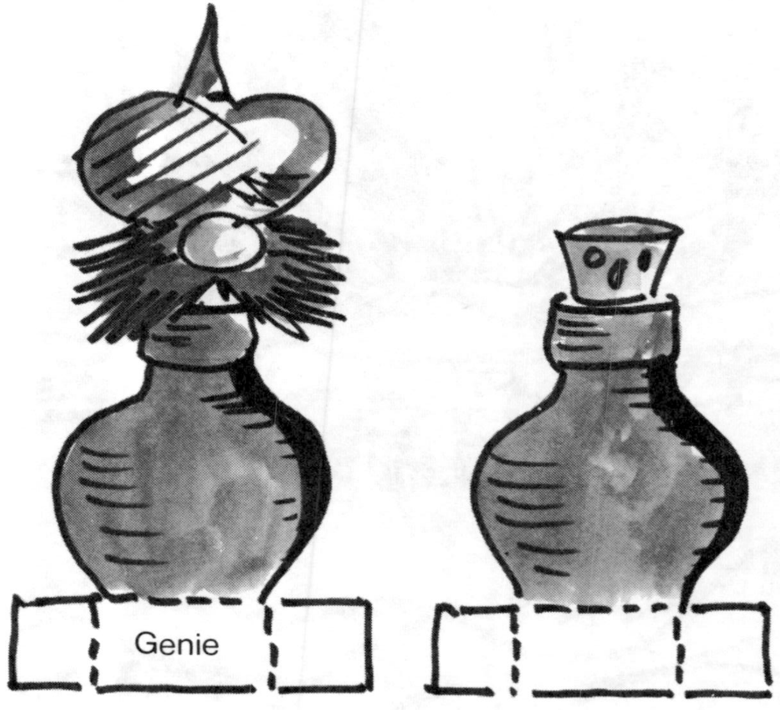
Genie

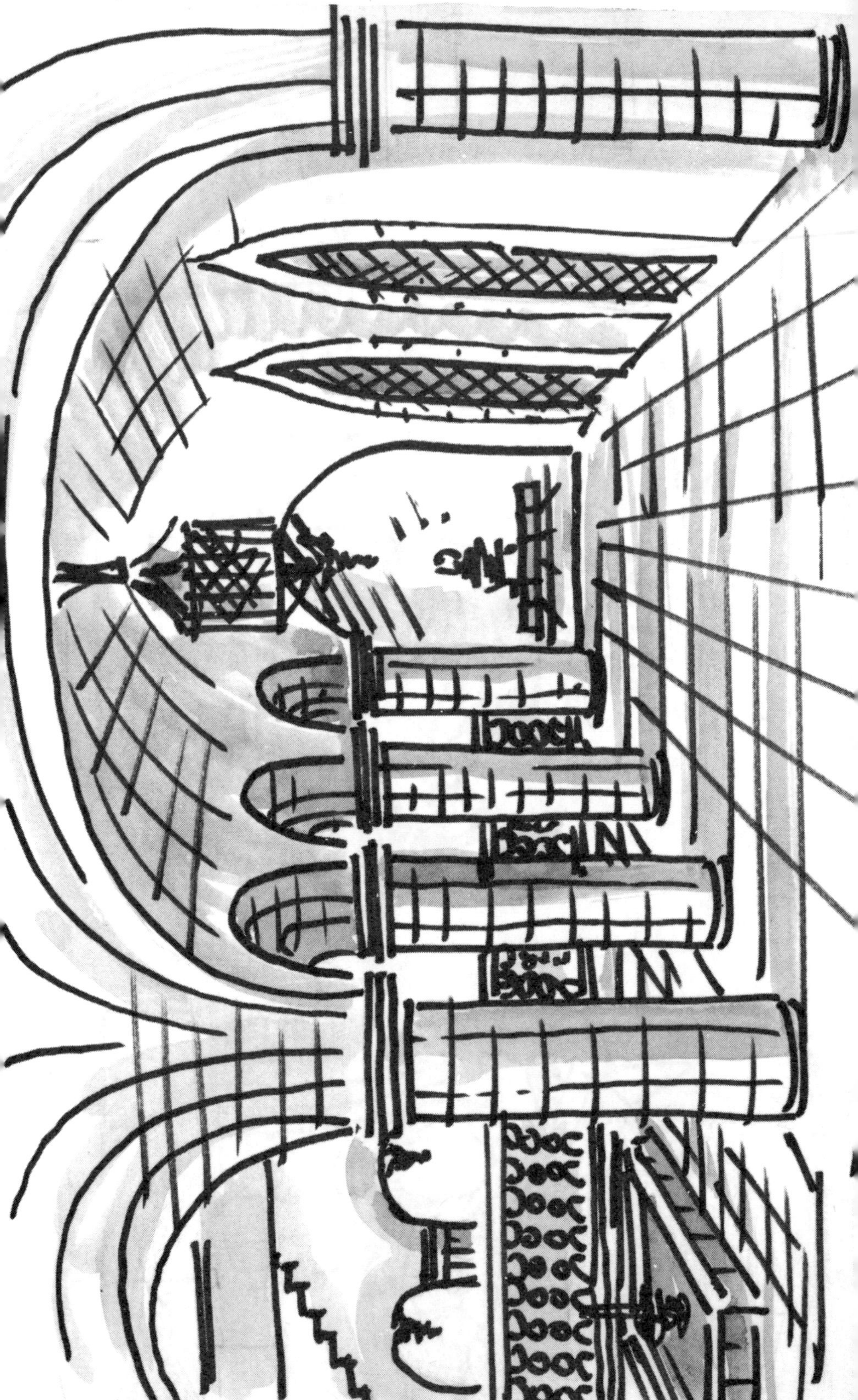

HOVERCARPET
OMAR TAXIS
BEND AT AN
ANGLE
Caliph
Omar

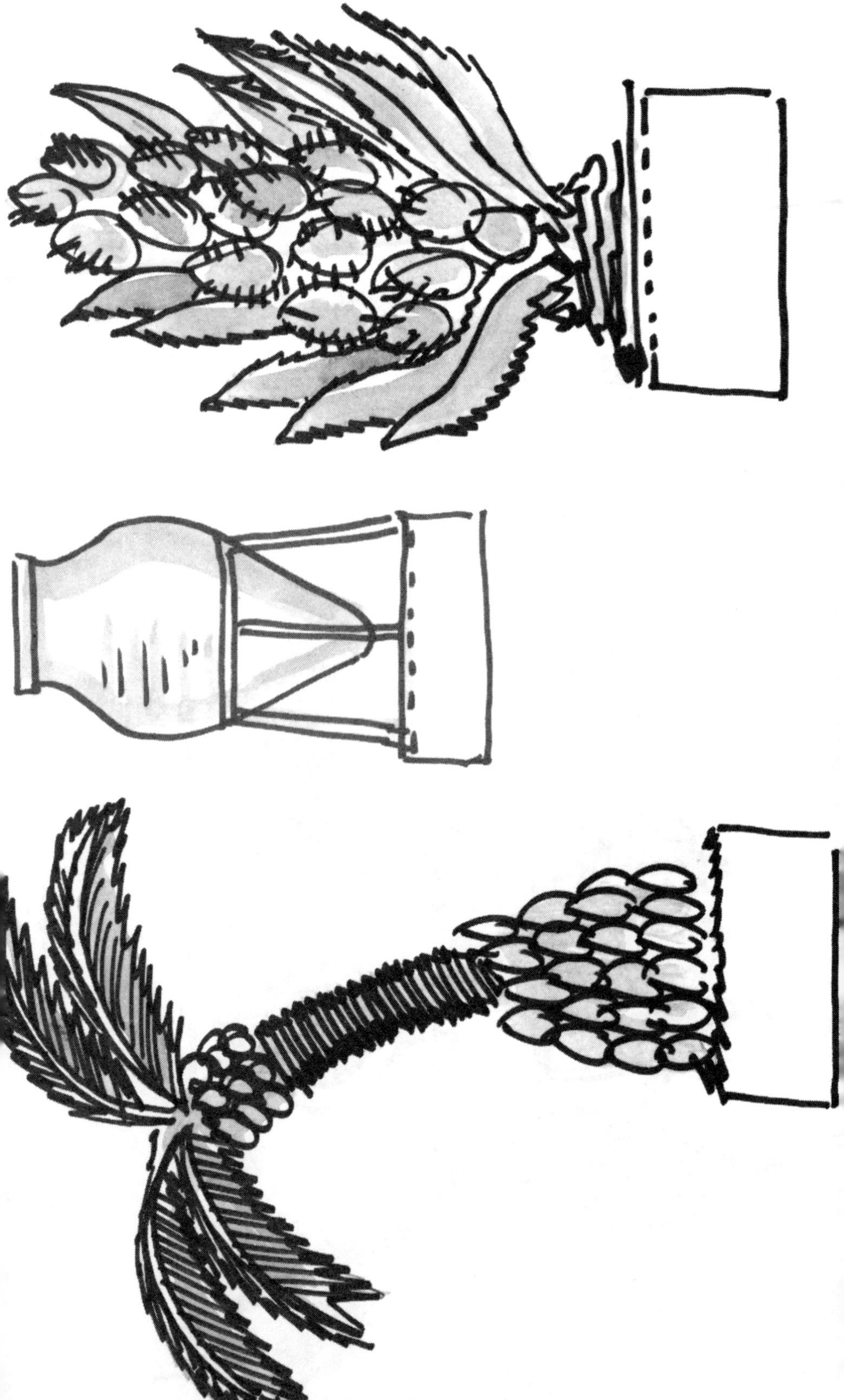

Prop C.

Prop D.

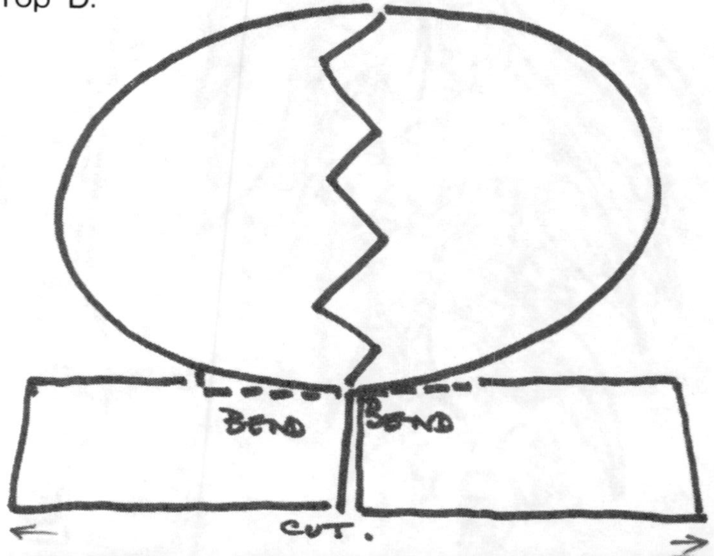

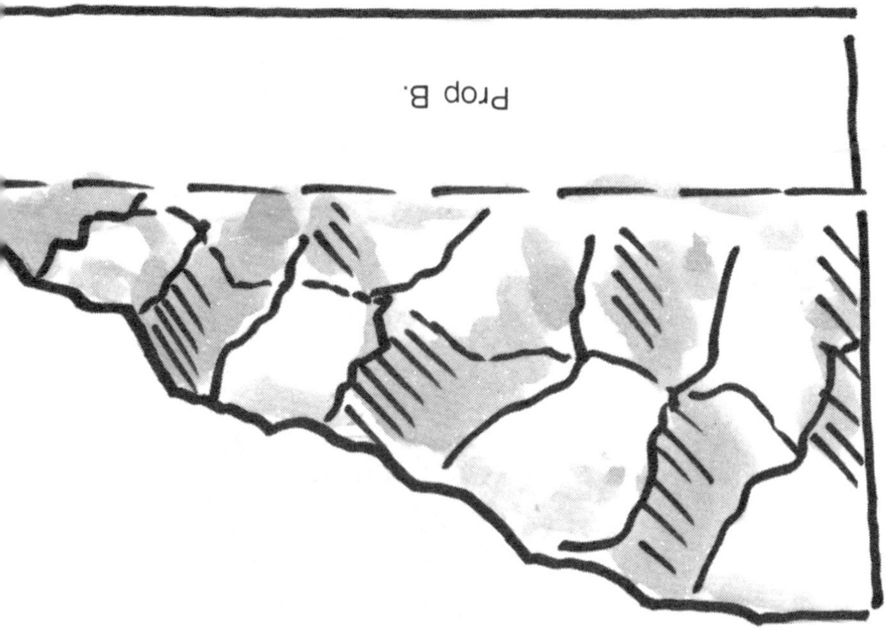
Prop B.

Prop A.

BEND

BEND

BEND

Vizier
Sheherezade
Caliph

BIG CHIEF CRAZY POTTY

When the American settlers decided to move from the Eastern States right across the vast wild west prairies towards California, they drove the huge herds of buffalo in front of them. Now, the buffalo were the wealth of the Red Indians — they provided warm clothes and tents, and horn handles for knives and tools, as well as milk for the young and food for everyone. As the buffalo were forced back by the arrival of the settlers' wagon trains on their feeding grounds, so the Red Indians had to move back with them.

This caused a lot of bad feeling between the settler Pottys and the Red Indian Pottys, and many a mass punch-up — or 'pottycree' — took place. Finally the crack regiment of Dog Soldiers, the 7th Cavalry, was sent in to make a peace treaty with Big Chief Crazy Potty and his son, Little Chief Sitting Potty.

Naturally, the Commanding Officer of the 7th Cavalry — Colonel Beauregard Potty — wanted to make the best deal possible for the settlers because he was coming up for retiring age, and would soon be leaving the 7th Cavalry to become a settler himself. Helped by some tricky and cunning lawyers, he drafted a treaty which was very unfair to the Red Indian Pottys. It gave all the best land to the settlers, especially land where Potty prospectors had found gold, and left only the poorer country and the desert to the Red Indians for their Potty reservations.

Luckily, the great Potty Scout Buffalo Bill, who had lived among the Indian Pottys for many years, spotted this mean trick and warned the Potty tribe about it. To his surprise, they didn't seem at all worried. Crazy Potty and Sitting Potty told him they didn't mind, as long as the 7th Cavalry and the President of the United States guaranteed that where the Potty tribe was encamped, there it would be allowed to stay for ever.

The 7th Cavalry eagerly agreed to these terms, and Colonel Beauregard Potty fell over himself to sign the treaty before the Red Indian Pottys could change their minds. They even smoked a pipe of peace together, which made the Indians feel very happy, and the Colonel very sick. The soldiers of the 7th Cavalry then rode off, chuckling to themselves because they thought they had fooled Big Chief Crazy Potty.

Buffalo Bill felt very glum about this piece of trickery and couldn't understand why Crazy Potty and Sitting Potty were dancing about so happily, whooping and yelling and waving their magnificent feathered head-dresses in the air. Then the Potty tribe took down their tepees and showed Buffalo Bill what was underneath — and at last he understood. Yes, sir — every one of those tepees concealed an oil drilling rig! And what's more, every one of them had struck oil — yes indeedy, folks! The Potty tribe did very well out of that treaty — so Big Chief Crazy Potty wasn't so crazy after all! As Buffalo Bill said, 'Well, sir, I guess you're sitting Potty — er, I mean, pretty!'

A Memorable Day At GROGGLETHORPE GRAMMAR SCHOOL

I always used to wonder where the Pottys went to school — it must be a very good one, I used to think, to have produced such geniuses as Professor Potsworthy, the compiler of the *Encyclopaedia Pottanica* (all five hundred and one volumes), and Dr Pottle, the brilliant medical specialist who first diagnosed Pottymania. Well, I found out where they were educated the other day when I visited that great Potty centre of learning, Grogglethorpe Grammar School.

The Headmaster, Mr Emmanuel Beeswax, B.A. (failed), University of Chipping Sodbury (Correspondence Course Division) — or, as he is better known, The Great Twit, met me at the station. (The village of Grogglethorpe is so small that it doesn't have any trains — just a station. Perched high on the moors, it's quite a difficult place to get to.) With Mr Beeswax was the Lower Master, whose traditional nickname is The Little Twit.

What an impressive sight Grogglethorpe Grammar School was, as we drove up the imposing great drive — all twelve feet of it! The huge plastic-ivy covered walls of crumbling plywood and plaster (bought second-hand from a film studio which had just completed a film about Oxford University) stood swaying in the wind which blew fiercely across the moors.

'Magnificent, isn't it,' said the Head Master, wiping away a tear of emotion.

'Beautiful, Head Master,' echoed the Lower Master — a Mr Braithwaite, and a right crawler if ever I saw one.

What a day that was. I didn't realise that a Potty education covers so much ground — chiefly because it's spread out over an area of five miles, owing to the flimsy buildings being blown about in the gales.

The Potty pupils certainly face a very heavy curriculum. The years they spend at Grogglethorpe are not by any means wasted. They spend most of their time rebuilding the school — it gets blown down quite regularly in the high winds.

'A Potty education is a useful education,' declared the Headmaster. 'And what's more, it's very healthy. Any boy who can survive his first term at Grogglethorpe is a very healthy specimen.'

'Mens sana in Sanitary Corpo,' quoted the Lower Master, and then, turning to me, he added for my benefit, 'That means a sane mind in a grubby body.'

Before I could put him right, I was being shown the Potty pupils at work. They are certainly an enterprising lot, I must say. Frankenstein Minor was just completing his first successful clockwork monster, while Jekyll Minor had twice turned himself into Hyde Major. And sport has an important place in the time-

table. Dracula Minimus, a very keen cricketer, was showing every sign of becoming a first-class bat when I watched him hanging upside down in the nets.

'Yes,' sighed the Headmaster proudly, 'do you know, we've got one lad here from America. He's been caught red-handed thieving, breaking and entering, forging documents and blackmailing the other lads — by gum, but in time that lad could end up as President of the United States.'

Before I could ask him what he meant, there was a tremendous BANG and the windows of the Headmaster's study shivered into a thousand tiny pieces. We rushed to see what had happened, and there, rising into the sky was the school clock-tower.

'Hurrah!' shouted the Lower Master. 'They've done it at last! The school Chemistry Society has succeeded in putting the clock-tower into orbit!'

'Yes,' said the Headmaster reflectively, 'but we're certainly going to miss Matron.'

And sure enough, waving frantically from the top of the tower as it disappeared into the clouds was the tiny Potty figure of Matron! Unbelievable!

ANSWERS

TO THE POTTY QUIZ

1 A nurdlum or a nigglum. Particularly bad moles are called 'nukky nigh noo nurdling little nigglums' (or 'niggling little nurdlums').
2 Marco Polo.
3 Because the early bird catches the Worm.
4 When it isn't fully grown.
5 You don't get any reply.
6 Captain ffanshawe and Baron von Spitfaster.
7 The pirate flag.
8 Five hundred and one.
9 Fireworks and spag-het (or spaghetti).
10 As this is a Potty question, there are two answers: either nineteen (see page **61**) or eleven (because Pottys are always a little short).
11 Worm Football, Mexican Snail Fighting, Snail Racing, Yeti Ski-Jumping and Slalom Racing.
12 Fourteen inches.
13 It's like a catastrophe, only twice as big.
14 No — but who cares!
15 A violin.
16 He only takes silver from his passengers.
17 Thames Conservancy Potty.
18 Dr Pottle.
19 Grroggplethorpe Grammar School.
20 Moleditz.

ANSWERS TO THE POTTY WORD GAME

Here are the eighty words that I found in POTTYMANIA (and some of them are pretty Potty hard!), but I wouldn't be surprised if there are even more to be made:

to, ta, top, ton, tot, toy, tip, tit, tin, tint, tiny, tap, tan, tat, tain, taint, mop, map, man, mat, matt, may, ma, mitt, mint, minty, main, many, mania, matin, moan, moat, my, myopia, pot, potty, point, paint, painty, pain, pant, pit, pity, pin, pint, piny, pat, pay, pan, pa, patio, patty, am, an, at, apt, any, ant, aim, ay, attain, amity, no, not, nip, nit, nap, natty, nay, yon, yap, yam, opt, oat, on, it, in, into, imp, inapt.